Therapy Skills for Healthcare:
An Introduction to Brief Psychological Techniques

Other Health & Social Care books from M&K include

Nurses and Their Patients: Informing practice through
psychodynamic insights
ISBN: 978-1-905539-31-4

Spiritual Assessment in Healthcare Practice
ISBN: 978-1-905539-27-7

Perspectives on Death and Dying
ISBN: 978-1-905539-21-5

The Clinician's Guide to Chronic Disease Management
for Long-Term Conditions: A cognitive–behavioural approach
ISBN: 978-1-905539-15-4

Research Issues in Health and Social Care
ISBN: 978-1-905539-20-8

Identification and Treatment of Alcohol Dependency
ISBN: 978-1-905539-16-1

Preventing and Reducing Aggression & Violence
in Health and Social Care: A holistic approach
ISBN: 978-1-905539-57-4

Improving Patient Outcomes
ISBN: 978-1-905539-06-2

Ward-Based Critical Care
ISBN: 978-1-905539-03-1

The ECG Workbook
ISBN: 978-1-905539-14-7

Therapy Skills for Healthcare:
An introduction to brief psychological techniques

Caroline Forrest

Illustrations by Caroline Firenza

Therapy Skills for Healthcare:
An Introduction to Brief Psychological Techniques
Caroline Forrest

ISBN: 978-1-905539-58-1

First published 2011

British Library Cataloguing in Publication Data

A catalogue record for this book is available from the British Library

Notice

Clinical practice and medical knowledge constantly evolve. Standard safety precautions must be followed, but, as knowledge is broadened by research, changes in practice, treatment and drug therapy may become necessary or appropriate. Readers must check the most current product information provided by the manufacturer of each drug to be administered and verify the dosages and correct administration, as well as contraindications. It is the responsibility of the practitioner, utilising the experience and knowledge of the patient, to determine dosages and the best treatment for each individual patient. Any brands mentioned in this book are as examples only and are not endorsed by the publisher. Neither the publisher nor the authors assume any liability for any injury and/or damage to persons or property arising from this publication.

To contact M&K Publishing write to:
M&K Update Ltd · The Old Bakery · St. John's Street
Keswick · Cumbria CA12 5AS
Tel: 01768 773030 · Fax: 01768 781099
publishing@mkupdate.co.uk
www.mkupdate.co.uk

Designed by Mary Blood
Illustrations © Caroline Firenza 2011
Typeset in 10pt ITC Giovanni Book
Printed in England by Reed's Printers, Penrith

Contents

Preface vii

About the author viii

Foreword ix

Acknowledgements x

Chapter 1 Introduction **1**

Chapter 2 Building rapport **9**

Chapter 3 Gathering information **15**

Chapter 4 Formulating goals **21**

Chapter 5 Understanding depression **27**

Chapter 6 Managing anxiety **47**

Chapter 7 Promoting behaviour change **61**

Chapter 8 Concluding comments **73**

References **79**

To my sister, Rosalind

Preface

A 'grand design' or not, every project requires us to go on a journey. With a nod to Channel 4's Kevin McCloud, the development of this book has been an interesting journey, populated with encounters, discussions and connections with many people – friends, family, patients and colleagues. Finding the best way to address people's interconnected physical and emotional health needs is an ongoing challenge because organisational and professional factors often seem to force their separation. When we work as nurses, doctors and therapists we learn how to offer practical help, prescribe or dispense medicines, and carry out tests and procedures. Separately, we may consider whether patients need a counsellor or psychiatrist, but we rarely offer consistently holistic care with a psychological focus.

I believe that mainstream healthcare is a good place to develop a more integrated approach to meeting these needs. This is where we can intervene early, to prevent long-term problems and reduce the stigma of mental illness by explaining and treating patients' symptoms in the context of their lives. Addressing physical and emotional needs together offers us the opportunity to help patients change and to manage ourselves better, so that we thrive rather than just survive in the caring professions.

This book is for anyone who feels psychological care is important and who wants to build on skills that improve their effectiveness with patients. I hope it will be of interest to those already working in mental health settings and to people in general practice, community and outpatient settings, whether they are doctors, nurses, occupational and physiotherapists or other professionals.

About the author

Caroline Forrest BSc (Hons), RN, MPH qualified as a nurse in 1997 after first completing a degree in Biology and Education. She worked for four years as a specialist renal nurse before spending a brief period in coronary care and other acute medical settings. She has spent nearly a decade in primary and community healthcare, including a period as a community matron. She has a Master of Public Health degree and a Diploma in Human Givens Therapy. She is currently working as a nurse in general practice with a special interest in diabetes.

Foreword

A consensus has emerged over the past ten years with regard to the care and treatment of people with common mental health problems, such as depression and anxiety. This consensus holds that people who experience psychological distress are best viewed within a paradigm that recognises the importance of being able to gain access to psychological therapies and approaches as part of a stepped approach to care. Caroline Forrest's book not only embraces the need for all health and social care staff to gain skills, knowledge and confidence in this area, but also provides the means by which the theory can be applied in practice.

As a senior mental health practitioner and researcher working in the field of primary care mental health, I have read and made use of a great many books, manuals and therapy guides. Most of these are written in language that is easily understood by highly trained mental health professionals and people trained in psychological therapies, but they are hard to digest and follow when accessed by non-specialist staff.

This book bucks the trend. It is written from a patient-centred perspective that reflects the pragmatic nature of the author who has worked in a variety of health settings. The efficient use of language and the precise, non-jargonised writing style make this a book that will be welcomed by a range of practitioners – from student nurses and social workers, to practitioners working in the community and primary care. I can also see this book becoming a useful companion to mental health nurses who wish to extend their knowledge of psychological therapy approaches.

This is an evidence-based book that draws on advanced communication approaches including motivational interviewing, solution-focused therapy and neuro-linguistic programming to guide the reader along a journey from assessment to behaviour change.

I feel confident that this well-written and pragmatic book will be enjoyed and utilised by health and social care practitioners for many years to come.

Dr Mike Scanlan
Nurse Consultant Primary Care
Changing Minds Centre, Northampton

Acknowledgements

I would like to thank a number of people for their support in writing this book.

My thanks go to Maggie Leathley, Bob Gardner, Chris Watson, and from M&K Publishing, Mike Roberts, without whom I would never have got started.

For comments, encouragement and inspiration, thank you to Iain Caldwell, Dave Tomson and Peter Tate and to my local GP colleagues Bryan Morland, Yolanda Diez and Kriss Owen.

I would like to thank Mary Hastings, Martin Smith, Caroline Savidge and Sue Smith for their ideas, and Mike Scanlan for his research contribution and feedback.

Finally, I am indebted to my family always for their support, and to Jane McGregor, Caroline Firenza and Maria Hampshire for knocking this book into shape.

CHAPTER 1
Introductory comments

In this chapter you will find out about defining symptoms, psychological distress and patient-centred consultations.

This book is about making the best use of the therapeutic relationship to address patients' needs in combination with existing clinical treatment. It describes techniques to help patients change behaviour and manage anxiety and depression by adopting a psychological approach to physical healthcare. The skills described have been developed in psychological therapies but they can readily be used as brief interventions in general healthcare settings. The techniques are drawn from disciplines such as cognitive–behavioural therapy (CBT), solution-focused therapy and systemic (family) therapy, which all focus on helping people solve current problems within a short timeframe. The principal theme is that social and psychological factors both contribute to physical and mental illness and can also form part of their treatment. A more psychological and patient-focused approach involves actively seeking patients' concerns and empowering them to draw on their own abilities to manage problems. We can begin to harness their resources by acting as a catalyst in helping them to make lasting changes that will reflect a more pro-active and sustainable use of services.

All the techniques can be used in daily clinical situations and, although some will be familiar, it is hoped that others may provoke an interest in developing skills further. The inclusion of chapters on anxiety and depression does not mean to imply that non-mental health staff should be able to manage all their patients' mental illness. Psychological techniques may be best used in combination with medication, social support and referral to specialist services. It is always vital to know when to refer for more intensive input but a lot can be done to address low-level mental illness and offer care alongside specialist treatment. Understanding the factors common to all health-related behaviours can help in more effectively addressing risky alcohol and drug use, over-eating and smoking. Although any healthcare intervention is relatively brief in the context of a patient's whole life, the judicious use of combined psychological and clinical skills can produce a truly rewarding outcome for clinicians and patients alike.

Defining a symptom

It is widely believed that psychological distress contributes to a large proportion of the workload in primary care, with between 30 and 60 per cent of all consultations in general practice either being about mental distress directly, or containing significant psychological issues (Asen *et al.*, 2009). It is even possible that psychosocial problems are more prevalent than physical disease, although physical symptoms may also be present. How and what patients present as symptoms will depend on a number of factors including how they believe they will be perceived by professionals. They will be influenced by their own beliefs about illness as well as advice from family and friends, information from the internet, and their current emotional state. If as clinicians we stick too rigidly to a medical model in treating illness we may find we simply match patient symptoms against a checklist, without acknowledging these wider issues. As both a general practitioner (GP) and anthropologist, Helman (2006) believed that any intervention in general practice should aim to treat both the physiological disturbance and restore the balance in a patient's life as a whole.

Some problems described as medically unexplained symptoms can be a particular challenge because patients may attend repeatedly for consultations. The lack of a satisfactory diagnosis can be frustrating for clinicians and can generate further anxiety for the patient who wonders why they feel unwell if there is apparently nothing wrong. Medically unexplained symptoms are often categorised as 'somatisation', which is the physical expression of underlying depression or anxiety. It is thought that bodily symptoms unexplained by an identifiable disease account for around 20 per cent of new episodes of illness in primary care, and as many as one-third of all medical outpatients (Royal College of Psychiatrists, 2009). Primary care in particular offers the opportunity to intervene early in mental health problems in a non-stigmatising way. The generalist, low-key nature of its encounters allows the mind–body interaction to be explored before a diagnosis or a referral needs to be made. For example, effective and timely help managing anxiety and panic attacks can prevent the subsequent development of disabling phobias or obsessive behaviours.

Psychological distress

Patients with severe and enduring mental illness will often be seen by specialist services where their mental health needs are prioritised but these patients also bear a disproportionate burden of chronic physical illness. Contributory factors include social and organisational issues. These patients will miss out on suitable care from their GP surgery or hospital if they have difficulty attending appointments for services that do not readily meet their needs. There is often a lack of expertise among mental health and general healthcare staff about each others' areas of work, which is not helped by the separation of the services. There are high levels of smoking, alcohol and other drug use, obesity, and poor social and employment opportunities in this group of patients, which makes them more likely to develop chronic illness and makes its management more difficult.

Mental illnesses range from depression, anxiety, obsessive–compulsive disorders, phobias and post-traumatic stress disorder, to lower-level 'sub-threshold' conditions that do not meet diagnostic criteria. However, these conditions still have a significant impact on people's well-being and use of services (Boardman et al., 2004) and they are often amenable to effective treatment in general healthcare settings. Depression is the most common mental health problem and it is expected to become the second leading cause of all (physical and mental) disease across the world by 2020 (Murray and Lopez, 1996). It seems to affect younger people and women disproportionately, although it is possible that men express depressed mood in different ways. With its peak onset now in young adulthood, there are serious social and economic implications for the future. Indeed, the direct healthcare costs of managing depression exceed those of hypertension and diabetes combined (Department of Health, 1996), before even considering other indirect financial and social consequences. Anxiety is a common source of distress that often co-exists with depression. The sensation of fear and the fight-or-flight response are normal human reactions and not necessarily a sign of pathology. However, excessive symptoms can be problematic. It is normal to experience a degree of anxiety when seeking help for worrying symptoms but this anxiety state is different from a lifelong habit or anxiety trait, which may be part of one's nature or due to learned behaviour. Anxiety disorders have been found in 10 per cent of women and 5 per cent of men (Meltzer *et al.*, 1995), with 25 per cent of people experiencing them at some stage in their lifetime. The average GP list may have around 400 patients in this category.

The proportion of healthcare resources devoted to all types of chronic disease

is increasing steadily. In both physical and mental illness, psychological factors will influence patient compliance to medication, understanding and management of potential complications, and appropriate use of services. Anxiety and depression are often associated with cancer and respiratory conditions and there is a strong association between depression and both diabetes and heart disease. Some studies even suggest that depression can more accurately predict adverse physical outcomes than any other factor. In the UK, screening questions for depression are now routinely incorporated into assessment of patients with these conditions, which has helped to raise awareness of their prevalence and association with physical illness. However, knowing how best to help depressed people once they have been diagnosed is the real challenge.

Patient-centred consultations

The various healthcare consultation models primarily developed within general practice focus on either clinician behaviour or on tasks that need to be carried out (Neighbour, 2005). There is broad agreement, however, that psychological and social factors should be incorporated into the assessment of patients' needs. Whatever the behavioural techniques – or processes – used, there are a number of tasks that should be achieved within the consultation. These can be summarised (Pendleton *et al.*, 2003) as follows:

• understand the problem

• understand the patient

• share understanding

• share decisions and responsibility

• maintain the relationship.

The therapeutic relationship has been central to the healing process across cultures and centuries. Evidence proves that the emotional connection and quality of communication between clinician and patient affects consultation outcomes more than any amount of medical knowledge (Greenberg, 2007; Royal College of Psychiatrists, 2009). However, patients' expectations of their doctor and other healthcare professionals will vary and they may be affected by age, culture, education and social class. Some patients may not wish to be involved in decision-making about treatment, but others will expect a much more collaborative approach. The availability of information via the internet means that clinicians no longer have control of 'medical knowledge' and the role is changing into that of 'interpreter of health information' (Tate, 2010). The use of information technology and hi-tech diagnostic procedures and treatments has changed the way clinicians consult with patients. The computer is a big part of the general practice consultation now and the expectations of healthcare – from patients, practitioners and governments – are rapidly evolving.

Motivational interviewing (MI) describes three different styles of communication in healthcare. These are: following, guiding and directing (Rollnick *et al.*, 2008). It is common for professionals trained in the Western medical model to have a strong *directing* style, which reflects a belief in a body of expert knowledge that should be transmitted to the patient. In contrast, a *following* style involves simply listening to the patient and letting them talk without interruption. Anyone who uses this style too much is likely to feel powerless to steer their consultations. They may be well-liked by patients but be seen as a 'soft touch'. However, a degree of 'following' or letting the patient talk is an essential part of all encounters with patients. The third communication style, *guiding*, is the most useful one when supporting patients to change their behaviour. It allows them to take the initiative, with a supportive clinician in the role of a mentor or objective friend. The guiding style conveys a sense of empowerment and helps the patient to build on their existing resources, channelling their motivations to produce successful change. Taking a psychological approach means being aware of how emotions may be expressed and then structuring our consultations and communication with patients accordingly. Mental distress is not just something that happens to other people – it affects all of us to some degree – and understanding how to manage our responses should be a priority for everyone working in healthcare. Some people instinctively tune in to other people's needs without realising they are doing it, but it also a skill that can be learnt. For a healthcare professional, self-awareness is important for gaining rapport with people with whom we may not instinctively feel comfortable. We need to be aware of how we are behaving and how our body language, our tone of voice and our choice of language may be interpreted by the patient. These skills are a key part of effective communication and help to foster good relationships.

Some clinicians fear there is not enough time to be patient-centred, or that they will have too little control over the consultation and its outcomes. However, good rapport and focusing on the patient's concerns increase the chances of identifying the problem quickly. If the patient trusts us, we can ask direct and difficult questions with confidence, including questions that identify physical disease, and do so in an encounter that is more relaxed and amenable to clearer thinking by both parties.

The techniques described in the following chapters have been taken or adapted from a range of texts and in some cases from more than one source. In order to make them as easy as possible to use, detailed references have not been provided in these sections. However, the reader can find most of the techniques described in more detail in the books listed in the Further Reading sections at the end of each chapter. There are illustrative case studies that deal with anxiety, depression and behaviour change, which are based on real patients, and 'ideas for practice' at the end of each chapter to help you get started.

CHAPTER 2
Building rapport

In this chapter you find out how to build rapport by noticing physiological and behavioural signs, recognising cat-like and dog-like behaviours, and matching the pace, movement and language of your patient. You will also learn how to break rapport with the patient when it becomes necessary.

At the core of any successful intervention is the relationship between the patient and the professional. The view of the relationship as therapeutic in itself is widely known. In 1957, Balint described the doctor as someone whose behaviour would alter the clinical outcome, who would be like a drug for the patient (Balint, 2000). This can be understood as part of the 'placebo effect', which is usually discussed in relation to prescribed medicines, but which is actually the effect of factors other than the pharmacological properties of the drug or treatment on the person taking it. Practitioners of medicine in different cultures across the world have always known that beliefs, expectations and a good healer–patient relationship are vital in helping with recovery or coping with illness (Helman, 2007). We need the perspective we gain from talking to other people to reassure us that we are normal and help us sort out our problems. This supportive part of the medical role is essential but may conflict with other expectations, such as the need to be rational and scientific or to use technology and drugs. These varying demands come from within the individual and professions, as well as from wider society.

As human beings we give and receive attention by interacting with other people. In general we prefer to spend time with like-minded people and may express ourselves more readily if we sense that another person is somewhat similar to us. If we have rapport with patients, we transmit a sense of connection with them. This process can begin with the first interaction in the consulting room and be conveyed by our body language, eye contact, tone of voice and language. Having a connection does not mean we necessarily like the patient, but it conveys respect for their point of view. Rapport is important for reducing the emotional temperature and making space to introduce new ideas. Patients need to form an attachment to our ideas before we can have any influence. Instead of telling them what to do, we need to have good rapport and then guide them towards our thinking (Molden and Hutchinson, 2006). The skills used in sales and marketing to win trust and influence people can be put to good use in healthcare. Our effect on the outcome, which in this case is to improve the patient's health, will often largely depend on how we get on with the person.

HOW TO

Build rapport

For more about the techniques and principles described below, see the Further Reading section at the back of this chapter.

Match pace, movement and language

People deep in conversation will unconsciously copy each other's body postures, movements, tone of voice, pace and breathing. Try to do this deliberately in consultations and notice the effect. Simply observing how well your body language, pace of talking and tone of voice match that of the patient is the first step.

• Be aware that the patient may be trying to interpret your body language as well, so if you cross your arms or face the computer this may be interpreted as disapproval or disinterest.

• Notice how much the patient gestures while they speak and how much eye contact they make. Try to act in a similar way yourself, but without making radical changes that feel unnatural or seem like mimicry.

• Notice the patient's choice of words, phrases and metaphors. Use one word from something they said when you respond to them, to help with rapport and signal that you are listening.

• Try not to automatically change the patient's descriptions of their symptoms to fit a medical model. Instead ask them to clarify what they mean to be sure they have been understood correctly.

Notice cat and dog styles

People's behaviour may be categorised as either more like a 'cat' or a 'dog' in nature. Someone cat-like will sit still when listening, and speak with a flat tone of voice, perhaps standing with their arms crossed over their body or by their sides. Cat-type behaviour is slightly aloof. The person appears confident and as if they are expecting respect, but they are not necessarily aware of how they may be perceived by others. Dog-like behaviour will appear with a more varied tone of voice. This person may stand with hands on hips, or sit forward when listening and respond to the other person by making encouraging sounds. People with dog-type mannerisms may appear less confident but they are more approachable and eager to please, and they generally like things to be clear – not complex.

• Notice how you and other people fit into these categories in different situations. A clash between the two styles makes rapport difficult, whereas being with someone whose style is similar to your own will feel instantly relaxing.

• Adopt some of the characteristics of a dog to match someone who may otherwise tune out and not hear your messages, or behave in a cat-style to convey qualities of credibility and self-assurance.

Notice physiological and behavioural signs

Signs such as skin colour, pupil size, voice depth and flow of speech, muscle tension, lines on the face and breathing patterns can all indicate the state a patient is in at any given moment. Their state may or may not be related to the reason for their attendance.

Do not make automatic assumptions, but use the signs to assess how receptive they may be at that time. Consider how much information they may be likely to take in and whether it is a good time to challenge them, or to address health fears or discuss behaviour change.

Try to deliver your most important messages when the patient is relaxed. If the patient's face suddenly looks less lined and their body relaxes, then it is likely that they are feeling less anxious.

• Notice when the patient has a relaxed face, is making eye contact with large pupils, and has a still body, which all indicate a receptive 'trance' state. A patient may appear glazed and not seem to be listening, however they may be thinking about something you have said and processing new information.

• Be comfortable with silence and give the patient time to think.

Breaking rapport

You can break rapport when time is short and you need to move on. There are several ways of doing this, and if the message is still not clear you will have to say something more directly.

• Deliberately mis-match your body language in order to do so without appearing rude.

• Change the volume and pace of your voice.

• Further shift your body movements away from the patient.

Ideas for practice

- Notice how well your body language matches that of the patient when it is someone with whom you feel comfortable and in agreement.

- Notice how well your body language matches that of the patient when it is someone who makes you feel awkward or whose views you are trying to challenge.

- Notice what happens if you alter your body language to be more like the second kind of patient. Does the rapport between you seem to improve?

Further reading

Grinder, M. (2009). *Charisma. The Art of Relationships*. Battle Ground, WA: Michael Grinder and Associates.

Molden, D. and Hutchinson, P. (2006). *Brilliant NLP. What the Most Successful People Know, Say and Do*. Harlow: Pearson Education.

CHAPTER 3
Gathering information

This chapter explains how to gather information about your patient in a number of ways, by observing their body language, by using the technique of family circles and by noticing the 'dance' we engage in with each other, and considering whether these symptoms serve any purpose. You will be reminded how to listen well and give your full attention.

The main purpose of a healthcare consultation is to find out what is happening to the patient and how they are feeling in order to identify the problem and find a solution. It is also expected that the clinician will provide information and offer advice. How this happens depends on a number of factors related to the clinician and patient, their relationship, and the multiple contexts in which they both function.

Frames are ways of understanding and organising the world. The medical model itself is a frame and the people we see as patients are only patients in the context of the healthcare system. They will also be members of families and wider social networks with roles and relationships that affect their self-image and their perception of any problems they may have. An important job for an effective practitioner is to reframe what the patient is describing: to consider the same facts in a different way. Patients come to see us for a different way of viewing their problems. In a sense they may be asking us, 'Is my problem a valid symptom in your medical model?'

The skills required to gather information and clearly understand the messages being transmitted are more complex than simply asking a set of pre-defined questions. For example, it may be necessary to explore a patient's understanding of their health. Someone expressing extreme beliefs may have an inflexible view of the world or could be influenced by strong emotions such as anger, depression or anxiety. Feelings alter thoughts, so it may help to challenge fixed views by encouraging alternative perspectives such as taking a step back to see the bigger picture or a longer view over time. Everyone needs attention. It is a basic human need throughout the lifespan without which babies fail to thrive and adults are vulnerable to mental ill-health. Listening well is a valuable skill that requires practice, but it helps us to gain useful information quickly. It leaves the patient feeling satisfied that their point of view has been heard as well as a sense that we have spent more time with them. If we ask the right kind of questions and pay attention to what is said and what is not said, we should easily gain the information needed to meet the goals of both patient and clinician.

HOW TO

Gather information

For more about the techniques and principles described below, see the Further Reading section at the back of this chapter.

Listen well and give your full attention

Everyone needs attention, but some people receive very little in their daily lives. Even if we disagree or wish to challenge the patient in some way, it is essential first to attend to their beliefs and feelings.

• Give the patient time to think. They need to process information and this ability will be affected by their levels of intelligence, stress and anxiety, physiological changes due to illness, and the natural cycles of hormones, ageing and the time of day. When we pause for a moment and let the patient express themselves, it can have a dramatic effect. If someone feels their story is important they are more likely to voice their concerns and get what they need from the consultation.

• Start by letting the patient speak and convey that you have heard them to help with rapport and lead to more productive outcomes.

• Reflect back to the patient what you think they have said to clarify that you have understood them correctly.

• Repeat a word or phrase they have used in your response, but do this carefully if the patient's language is very different from your own.

• Do not interrupt the patient too much, but do follow up points that may be relevant to the current problem. Good listening should make it easier to ask the right questions. The important issues may not be ones that were anticipated before the patient spoke, but once established they may indicate the cause and management of the problem.

Notice eye movements

One of the techniques used in neuro-linguistic programming (NLP) involves observing people's eye movements as a way of understanding their thinking style. This may be predominantly one of four modes: visual, auditory, kinaesthetic or internal dialogue. Someone processing information in a *visual* way, such as remembering or imagining what something would look like, will move both eyes upwards to one or the other side whilst they are thinking. In an *auditory* mode, eye movements will be sideways. *Kinaesthetic* thinkers or people with an *internal dialogue* will look downwards.

• Observe these eye movements when you are talking to patients. They are due to the connections between the eyes and certain functional parts of the brain. You will be able to notice that they are visualising a possibility, or are deep in thought, or when they are remembering how something sounded to them.

• Notice whether the patient stares. A patient who is staring directly at you while you are talking is probably receptive and ready for new ideas and information.

• Look out for hand gestures. Someone with a strong internal dialogue may place a hand on the side of their face or stroke their chin. They may want to say something, or they may just be thinking.

• Keep aware of eye contact. The degree of eye contact may depend on the patient's level of confidence, but they may also be watching your responses before deciding whether to trust you and tell you more.

Consider whether the symptom serves a function

Sometimes symptoms do not seem to be a direct consequence of a physical problem or physiological disturbance, but have a more complex origin. For example, the symptom may be considered as an entry ticket to see the doctor – not that it is unreal or invalid, but rather that distress seems more acceptable as a physical symptom. Emotional disturbances change physiology and can affect both immune and neurological functions. Physical symptoms may be the way the patient experiences and defines the problem. Family (systemic) therapy describes how the symptom may have become part of a family or relationship and affect how members relate to each other.

• Ask questions about physical symptoms like headaches. A headache may be a new parent's subconscious expression of resentment on losing their old way of life. It may be an excuse not to take part in certain activities or conversations, either consciously or otherwise. It can also become the focus of the relationship with its presence or absence constantly noted: 'So your headache has gone now you are about to play football?'

• Question the function of the symptom with care and respect. This allows both patient and clinician to wonder whether the symptom is a metaphor for something else and whether it represents a feeling that is difficult to express. Even pain that has an organic explanation, such as arthritis, may have a place in the family that affects how it is managed.

• Ask whether the symptom stops the patient doing something they do or don't want to do.

• Ask whether the symptom affects other roles and relationships in the family or workplace?

Create family circles

Family therapy involves a technique called 'family circles' whereby patients are asked to place themselves in relation to significant other people and things in their lives. Draw a large circle on a piece of paper and explain to the patient that this represents their life as it is now. Then ask them to draw some smaller circles that stand for people who are important to them, their hobbies, work, or pets or anything they choose, and their illness if they want to (and not forgetting themselves).

The patient can complete it on their own, either in the consulting room or after they leave. The circles may be large or small, overlapping or far apart, or inside or outside the main circle. Each one should be labelled.

This is a useful way for bringing other people into the picture and provides a sense of who or what is most helpful, problematic, or simply present. The technique can even surprise the patient, who may not have realised the significance of a particular aspect or person in their life. By naming a condition such as anxiety or diabetes and placing it with reference to other parts of their life, the patient can begin to see its impact and how they may want it to change.

Drawing the circles can help a patient gain a more objective view of their difficulties and it may show how much the development or continuation of the problem is affected by something else. You can use the family circles to prompt further questions.

• Ask about any circle that is particularly big.

• Ask about any circle that is on its own, apart from the others.

• Ask about any circle that is completely contained by another.

• Ask what a particular person in their life might say about that if they were present.

Notice the dance

Systemic therapy recognises what it calls the habitual 'dance' that we engage in repeatedly with our friends, family and colleagues. We all assume roles and convey expectations of others' responses that have the movement of a dance. If one person behaves in one way, then another person will do something as a result, which then makes something else happen … and so on.

In healthcare settings, the dance may be one of repeated consultations with the same patient. The steps will become familiar to both parties and may be strangely comforting or frustrating. A couple in a close relationship may show a predictable pattern of behaviour when one of them tries to instigate change or complains that they feel unwell, and the other provides well-rehearsed responses.

Either you or the patient can alter the footing or introduce a new step to alter this dance. A momentary shift can illuminate the old habit and introduce the possibility of change.

Ideas for practice

- **Wait before you ask your opening question. See what happens.**
- **Pause, when you would normally carry on talking. See what happens.**
- **Use a word the patient has just used when you respond to them, to clarify what they mean, or simply use it in your next question. Notice whether they seem to be more engaged with what you are saying.**
- **Think of a patient you find difficult to help. Imagine asking them some questions about how other people view their problem.**
- **Ask them what is different when the problem isn't so bad.**

Further reading

Asen, E., Tomson, D., Young, V. and Tomson, P. (2009). *Ten Minutes for the Family. Systemic Interventions in Primary Care.* London: Routledge.

Molden, D. and Hutchinson, P. (2006). *Brilliant NLP. What the Most Successful People Know, Say and Do.* Harlow: Pearson Education.

Tate, P. (2010). *The Doctor's Communication Handbook*, 6th edn. Oxford: Radcliffe Publishing

CHAPTER 4
Formulating goals

In this chapter you will find out more about how to set therapy goals with your patient. Family circles can be employed here too, as well as the so-called miracle question, with good use of open questioning and assessment of problems using a scale.

The current trend towards a more patient-centred approach to healthcare is reflected in the use of terms such as concordance instead of compliance. It reflects a departure from a paternalistic model to one that views the patient as an equal partner in decision-making. Some sceptics assume patient-centred care means giving patients whatever they want, regardless of clinical need, but this is not its true essence. It is more about actively exploring their concerns and explicitly incorporating their wishes into treatment decisions. Some patients will undoubtedly expect clinicians to decide what is best for them, but their participation can still be sought. Indeed, they may wish to become more actively involved over time if they feel their opinion is valued. Some consultation models describe a distinction between the clinician's focus on pathology or 'disease' and the patient's focus on their experience of 'illness' (Kurtz and Silverman, 1996).

The benefit of being more patient-focused from the start is that the time will be used to best effect. The clinician may be aware of risks that are unknown to the patient, that need addressing, and the patient will certainly expect them to do so.

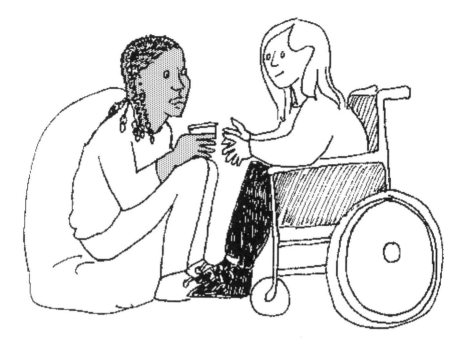

In a problem-solving situation such as the clinical consultation it is necessary to identify the problem and then break it down into manageable steps. In brief psychological therapy settings are defined and goals set to help the client build a sense of competence and control. It is suggested that *problems* should be jointly identified between therapist and client but *goals* should be determined by the clients (O'Hanlon and Weiner-Davis, 2003). Patients' and clinicians' perceptions of a problem may vary and need to be clarified to make decision-making purposeful.

The clinical goals may include the need to meet targets and follow guidelines, manage prescribing costs or reduce patient dependence on health services. The patients' goals may be quite different and both may change during the consultation as the issues are discussed. However, patients are more likely to participate in a plan of care if they have some emotional investment in it. O'Connell (2005) explains how most people want to work towards goals of their own choosing and, whilst appearing to comply with external ones, will find other ways to sabotage them.

HOW TO

Set goals with patients

For more about the techniques and principles described below, see the Further Reading section at the back of this chapter.

Use open questions

Open questions encourage patients to imagine a different future. They can visualise and describe it instead of dwelling on past failures.

- Unpick vague statements such as 'I just want to feel better' or 'I don't want to feel depressed'.

- Explore how this will look in terms of activities, relationships or functioning.

- Help the patient visualise success and measure progress by asking what would be a sign that things were still moving in the right direction.

- Generate some open questions to elicit 'change talk' according to the acronym DARN:

  D esire: 'What do you want, like, wish, or hope for?'

  A bility: 'What is possible?', 'What can or could you do?' or 'What are you able to do?'

  R easons: 'Why would you make this change?', 'What would be some of the specific benefits?' or 'What risks would you like to reduce?'

  N eed: 'How important is this change?' or 'How much do you need to do it?'

Use the miracle question

This technique from solution-focused therapy asks the client to imagine how things would be different if their problem magically disappeared overnight. It encourages the use of visualisation and imagination which are powerful tools that can help to bring about the desired changes, and sometimes the patient can see they are not as far away from their goals as they thought. The full version of the miracle question is as follows:

'I'm going to ask you a kind of strange question now. Suppose you go to bed and to sleep tonight as usual … and while you are asleep a miracle happens … and the problem that brought you here today is solved. But you are asleep and don't

know that it has been solved. What will be the first small signs that this miracle has happened and that the problem is solved?'

• Try a briefer version of the question or use it to inform your discussion with the patient: 'If this problem X could magically disappear, how would things be different?'

• Provide further prompts if necessary, and encourage the use of visualisation and imagination, with questions such as: 'How would you look?' or 'What would you be doing?' or 'How would you and other people know that the problem had gone away?' When the patient realises their goals are not as far away as they thought, they can develop their ideas and make further progress.

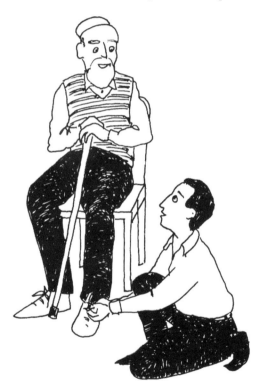

Assess problems using a scale

It can be useful if patients give their problems a score for the severity of some physical symptom or to describe the level of their mood.

• Ask the patient to rate their degree of pain or level of mood from zero up to 10.

- Use the score to encourage discussion about variability in symptoms and how things can be better, explaining that everything changes and will not be bad all the time.
- Ask what it would take to move their score from 4 to a 5, for example, or how things would be different if their pain or distress were as low as 3.
- Use the idea to set realistic goals such as turning down the dial or reducing the level of intensity of a problem, rather than expecting to eliminate it.
- Discuss how other people might react if their score were better. Patients may realise that behaving differently themselves could bring about the desired change.

Use family circles

These were described in full in Chapter 3. Family circles can be useful for looking at things from a different perspective. They can offer a bird's-eye view of the patient's problems in the context of their interests, work, family and friends.

- Use the circles to identify specific areas that could be changed. The patient could, for example, make a circle for illness smaller, move a circle outside the main circle, or shift the position of a circle so that it is not in the way of other circles.
- Use the circles to compare how things are now with how the patient would like them to be. For example, ask where the illness is now in their life, what it looks like, whether it is in the way of their relationships and where they would like it to be.

Ideas for practice

- Ask how things would be different if the problem had disappeared. Get as much detail as possible and notice how the patient appears when describing this situation.
- Ask the patient how a friend or family member would behave differently if their problem were less apparent.
- Ask what would be a sign that things were improving for the patient.

Further reading

Asen, E., Tomson, D., Young, V. and Tomson, P. (2009). *Ten Minutes for the Family. Systemic Interventions in Primary Care.* London: Routledge.

Macdonald, A. (2008). *Solution-Focused Therapy. Theory, Research and Practice.* London: Sage Publications.

O'Connell, B. (2005). *Solution-Focused Therapy,* 2nd edn. London: Sage Publications.

O'Hanlon, B. and Weiner-Davis, M. (2003). *In Search of Solutions. A New Direction in Psychotherapy.* New York: WW Norton.

Rollnick, S., Miller, W.R. and Butler, C.C. (2008). *Motivational Interviewing in Health Care. Helping Patients Change Behaviour.* New York: The Guilford Press.

Tate, P. (2010). *The Doctor's Communication Handbook,* 6th edn. Oxford: Radcliffe Publishing.

CHAPTER 5
Understanding depression

This chapter will explain how to consider various long-term strategies, paying attention to the patient's physical and emotional health needs, their degree of optimism and compassion, personal values and need for a balanced life. A number of cognitive and behavioural techniques will then be discussed to help you challenge harmful thinking, introduce uncertainty to fixed beliefs, and change patterns of activity. The effects of depression are described, and the importance of separating the person from the problem in offering useful problem-solving guidance. The importance of developing interpersonal skills, assertiveness and self-confidence for people with depression will also be discussed, and two case studies are provided to illustrate how depression may present and how it might be managed.

Depression has been around for centuries but is becoming increasingly common and is affecting people at an ever younger age. Although it may be triggered by difficult life events it is not an inevitable consequence of them. Instead it is often due to unhelpful ways of thinking and having unrealistic expectations of people or situations. Many depressed people feel anxious or angry and too ashamed to seek help. They may fear being diagnosed with a mental illness, or not recognise that their problems are due to depression. They may not want medication or counselling, or may simply not believe in it, and think they should be able to 'pull themselves together'. The condition has a significant impact on society because people are unable to fulfil their potential and often have relationship problems with family, friends and colleagues.

Some of the defining symptoms of depression are lethargy and withdrawal from normal activities, changes in appetite, poor sleep, low mood, difficulty concentrating and often excessive guilt and self-blame. If the symptoms are numerous, intense and long-lasting it is defined as 'major depression', but the condition can also be less intense and more episodic in nature. Depression may be severe and alternate with periods of mania, such as in bipolar disorder, or be little more than a response to life stresses causing temporary withdrawal from normal activities.

Treatment for depression may involve social, psychological or pharmacological interventions, or a combination of these things. Social factors such as housing and employment are often important in depression, but changing such factors directly may be difficult for a healthcare practitioner. Discussion about the use of antidepressants is beyond the scope of this book, but it is widely considered elsewhere.

Instead, this chapter describes some long-term strategies and cognitive, behavioural and interpersonal techniques that help to lift depression. Treatment should have two principle aims: to solve any current problems, and to reduce unwanted symptoms. We can raise patients' expectations for improvement with a hopeful and positive attitude towards managing depression. If we have good rapport with the patient, and can explain what depression does to them and how they can begin to feel better, then we are likely to be on the right track.

Normalising depression and offering hope

If you only do one thing – normalise the depression and offer hope for relief. As one general practitioner said: 'I think depression is the one thing we can really do something about in primary care. We can't replace a hip but we can help lift depression, which can be as significant, if not more so. You can see people really transformed.'

There are many ways to help patients who are suffering with low mood or depression. The first is to reassure them that the problem is common and manageable:

- Depression is largely the result of how people think about events. By noticing how they respond to life's challenges, patients can then choose to think and behave differently.

- Depression is not a sign of weakness and neither should it be a part of anyone's identity.

- Depression is no more than its symptoms, which can be resolved by increasing a sense of control, improving social relationships, and learning to view things in a non-negative way.

Developing long-term strategies

If possible, we should encourage patients when they are feeling stronger to develop their resilience and social support to reduce the risk of subsequent depressive episodes. Identifying potential trigger factors or vulnerabilities may help them feel more in control.

Attend to physical health

Good quality sleep, a nourishing diet and regular exercise all contribute to emotional well-being. Some people are particularly prone to feeling low when they are tired, so getting adequate sleep may be a priority for them. Exercise can help to lift mood by the physiological changes that occur and sometimes by distracting them from repetitive thoughts.

Alcohol can have a negative effect on mood because the initial feelings of relaxation or euphoria may be followed by worsening of mood. Smoking may increase or restart during vulnerable times and can have a detrimental effect on both physical and mental health.

Recognising emotional needs

In addition to physical needs, we also have emotional ones that affect our mental health. These include the need to feel part of a wider community and to share an emotional connection with people. To feel well, we need to give and receive enough attention and be accepted for who we are. We also need some privacy and time to ourselves (Griffin and Tyrrell, 2004). Depressed people commonly withdraw and spend too much time alone, but depression can also occur if someone is constantly busy and has no time to themselves to pause and reflect.

Other emotional needs include those for status and respect and to feel a sense of meaning and purpose through achieving things. These needs may be met in many different ways. Someone who is retiring from a job that gave them a sense of status and purpose in life may need to actively seek out other means of getting those needs met outside of work. And someone who has just become a parent may feel they are no longer connected to other people and receive little attention themselves, so they may need to develop new and different relationships.

Acknowledging personal values

People's values will be shaped by their upbringing, but they may change over a lifetime. They vary between extremes, such as focusing entirely on the self, to focusing on other people; from maintaining tradition, to striving to make changes; from being emotional, to being more logical; from taking risks to playing safe (Yapko, 1997). Being able to clarify one's personal values gives someone the opportunity to try and live in a way that is compatible with them. Depression may occur when there is a conflict between what someone thinks is important and what they are actually doing, or when there is a mismatch between an individual's values and those of their society. It can also be useful to assess other people's values particularly in personal relationships, to see if they are compatible with one's own.

Aiming to create a balanced life

A life that includes supportive relationships, time to relax, some meaningful activities such as work and hobbies as well as some time alone will help resist depression, especially if someone's low moods stem from one part of their life (Butler and Hope, 2009). Good mental health requires people to be flexible in adapting to changes, to be able to deal with losses and find comfort using their personal resources. Depression is more likely if very strong and inflexible values mean that the emphasis is on one particular aspect of life, to the detriment of others. However, outstanding achievements often occur because of great focus in one particular area, so personal drive and values will determine the level of risk-taking in this regard.

A balanced life means making time for relaxation and enjoyable activities. Having light relief from some of the more difficult challenges is important for everyone.

Developing optimism and compassion

A flexibly optimistic attitude – not viewing set-backs as pervasive, personal or permanent – will reduce the risk of developing depression (Seligman, 1998). In this context, optimism means developing a neutral or non-negative way of viewing things. When faced with adverse events, people generate a set of beliefs that either help or hinder them in coping with those events. People who are prone to depression tend to have a pessimistic explanatory style and reach negative conclusions about why things have happened. This habit of negative thinking combined with a tendency to dwell on thoughts rather than taking action is a potent combination for the development of depression.

Becoming more compassionate means learning to direct attention in a helpful way, and to think and behave with kindness and warmth towards oneself and others (Gilbert, 2009). Compassion can be developed using imagery and relaxation techniques. People who are depressed can be very self-critical and unkind to themselves. They may be equally hard on other people, sometimes with quite unrealistic expectations of what those people should offer them. Conversely, they may be too generous towards others, with poorly-defined personal boundaries that make them vulnerable to feeling hurt and disappointed (Yapko, 2009).

Cognitive techniques: Addressing thoughts

Depression can be the consequence of a particular way of reacting to life's challenges. Habitually responding to events by dwelling on negative explanations will worsen a person's mood because those thoughts trigger further negative emotions and behaviour. The threshold for these thoughts and behaviours will also become lower over time with repeated experiences (Crane, 2010). However, the cycle can be broken by helping people to notice and respond in new ways, to behave differently, and feel better as a consequence. Cognitive therapy is based on the two principles, that how we interpret what happens in the world affects both how we feel and what we do, and that we can change one by changing the other. Here are some examples of unhelpful thinking styles that are common in depression:

- Dichotomous 'black and white' or fixed thinking.
- Predicting negative outcomes and magnifying the implications of an event.
- Guessing what people are thinking and drawing conclusions for which there is no evidence.
- Over-generalising and drawing a general conclusion on the basis of one event.
- Mental filtering or bias, and paying attention only to the negative features of a situation.
- Personalising, by relating external events to oneself in an unwarranted way.

HOW TO

Challenge harmful thinking

For more about the techniques and principles described below, see the Further Reading section at the back of this chapter.

Introduce uncertainty to fixed beliefs

Automatic explanations for events are usually distortions of reality, so try to offer an alternative perspective for the patient to consider. The fixed and negative thought processes of depression do not respond well to rational argument. Try instead to appeal to the patient's imagination.

• Use metaphors and stories to help change their thought processes at a subconscious level, rather than discussing their specific problems.

• Get the patient to imagine putting on a new pair of glasses with a different coloured lens so they view the world differently.

• Try the 'My friend John' technique and talk about another (maybe imaginary) person who had similar concerns and managed them in an effective way.

• Point out past successes, and challenge negative statements such as 'I can't do anything about it'.

• Ask the patient what they would say to a friend with similar difficulties. Ask why they wouldn't talk to them in the negative way they talk to themselves.

Separate the person from the problem

It will help the patient if they regard their depression as something separate from themselves.

• Talk about the depression as something separate by asking what makes them vulnerable to depression and how depression makes them think differently.

• Encourage the patient to visualise the depression as a thing, such as a dark cloud that they can imagine drifting away.

• Suggest that they give their depression a name (Samuel Johnson and Winston Churchill called it The Black Dog) to help make it separate and manageable. (Or some people may choose to swap the metaphorical dog for a real dog – an excellent antidote to low mood.)

Distinguish between thoughts and facts

The depressed patient is likely to be worrying about past or imagined future events, rather than focusing on what is actually happening now, and will often feel powerless to effect change.

• Encourage the patient to notice that their thoughts are often ruminations on past events, or repetitive imaginings of the 'what if?' type, rather than worries about any current events.

- Ask what 'depression' means to them. How it makes them feel. How they act differently. How do other people respond when they are depressed?

- Try to get specific details about what is happening to the patient and what is actually a problem, because they may be feeling overwhelmed.

- Explain to the patient who makes consistently negative statements that depression often causes people to make sweeping generalisations.

- Encourage them to think of alternative thoughts to their automatic explanations for events. Aim to generate as many alternatives as possible.

- Introduce possibilities to the patient that focus their attention on other people's feelings, to counteract the over-personalised bias of depression.

- Suggest that the patient writes down or voices out loud what they are thinking, to consider their troubles more objectively.

Choose where to focus attention

Distraction is a useful skill. The brain can only focus on one thing at once, so get the patient to practise focusing elsewhere, even if only for short periods. An undue focus on one problem area can spill over into the rest of their life. Encourage the patient to compartmentalise their problems, and so reduce their impact. Someone with trouble at work might focus on their pets, friends, family or hobbies to remind them that they have other things that define and occupy them.

• Encourage the patient to focus their attention on other people's feelings, to counteract the over-personalised bias of depression.

• Suggest that the patient listens for sounds as they walk down the road, looking at everything around them. They can imagine they are describing things to someone who is not able to see, or smell or taste the food they are eating, for example.

• Ask the patient to sit down each evening and recall three good things that happened that day, if someone smiled at them, or made a drink for them, or showed some interest in them.

Behaviour therapy: Taking action

Part of the cycle of depression is that low mood reduces motivation to take part in socialising and other activities. This in turn reduces the benefits of perspective and interaction with other people, encourages a focus on worries, and contributes to further isolation. The consequent loss of confidence in managing social interactions makes it even less likely that the person will get involved in their normal activities.

Tiredness is common with depression, too, and may be due to excessive worrying and poor sleep. Griffin and Tyrrell (2006) believe that we deal with undischarged emotions from the day during the dream phase of sleep, and that depressed people have much greater emotional burdens than others. People who are depressed therefore dream more, using more energy, and have less time for physically restorative sleep, leading to the feeling of tiredness on waking.

A behavioural approach to depression requires that patients get involved in activities to make themselves feel better. Simply doing different things or the same things in another way can generate motivation to do more. The key is persuading people to take action in the absence of a genuine desire to do so. Skills in rapport-building and engaging with the patient are crucial in achieving this shift. Depression robs people of their sense of humour and self-esteem. From us they need positive feedback, support and encouragement. They need to believe that they can feel better.

Change patterns of activity

For more about the techniques and principles described below, see the Further Reading section at the back of this chapter.

Describe the effects of depression

To someone with depression, even simple things can seem very difficult. Depression can limit their activity in the same way as a physical illness. People with depression are often very hard on themselves, and may have perfectionist tendencies.

• Explain that low mood reduces their motivation to engage in enjoyable activities (as well as chores and tasks) which can further worsen the patient's mood and provide more things to worry about.

• Recognise any achievement of the patient – however small it might be.

• Explain how usually simple things can become very difficult, which is directly due to the depression, therefore the patient should feel pleased even when they do normal things.

• Encourage the patient to push themself to do slightly more than they are currently doing, even though the depression can limit their activity in the same way as a physical illness.

Set activity goals

Achievable tasks or activities will build self-confidence of the patient with depression, and physical exercise will make them feel better and increase their motivation for doing or taking part in other things.

• Agree a task or activity goal, together with a timescale. Make it easily achievable to build up the patient's sense of self-confidence.

• Aim to include both exercise and activities with other people. If the patient claims to be too tired, explain that they will not feel more tired by doing exercise, but they are very likely to feel better.

• Explain to the patient that motivation improves after taking part in activities, so even if they feel unmotivated they should do something anyway.

• Encourage the patient to focus on the activity while they are doing it, and to become more 'mindful' or aware of what is happening in the present moment.

• Suggest to the patient that all forms of exercise will be good, but exercising while focusing on the physical sensations of movement is even better.

Think about problem-solving

People feel better when their brains are actively engaged in solving problems, which is easier to do if the problems are clearly identified and broken down into achievable steps. You can use the SMART acronym for setting their goals:
S pecific
M easurable
A chievable
R elevant
T imed.

• Explain to the patient that they will feel better when their brains are actively engaged in solving problems, rather than ruminating on things beyond their control.

• Try to identify problems that may be causing the depressed mood that need to be solved, and break them down into achievable steps. Even if the underlying issues are unclear or difficult to alter, addressing additional problems that have arisen from the depression is still beneficial.

• Help the patient to define the specific problem or problems and choose goals that are SMART (specific, measurable, achievable, relevant and timed).

• Generate some possible solutions and select, implement and evaluate them.

Interpersonal skills: Improving relationships

Depression can be a social problem related to lack of meaningful connections with other people. A lot of psychological distress is directly caused by poor relationships, but interpersonal problems also arise from the negative thoughts and behaviours that make depressed people difficult to connect with. Depressed people tend to have more conflict in their personal lives, fewer supportive networks of friends, and less well-developed social skills. The solution to depression may also be largely social in nature (Yapko, 2009). Low self-esteem, negative expectations and a lack of assertiveness can mean that the skills needed for healthy interaction with other people are not present and the depressed person repeatedly forms damaging relationships. By encouraging people to define personal boundaries and convey to others the right messages about themselves, they can begin to view depressed mood as just a minor and manageable inconvenience.

HOW TO

Develop assertiveness skills and improve self-confidence

For more about the techniques and principles described below, see the Further Reading section at the back of this chapter.

Improve assertiveness

Assertiveness is about fairness. Everyone's needs, desires and feelings are equally valid. The patient needs to be able to say 'No' politely if they are simply trying to keep someone happy and their own rights are being ignored. Avoiding conflict is not helpful because it sends the message that the patient does not value themselves greatly. Learning not to guess other people's feelings and managing criticism in a balanced way are all useful skills.

• Explain to the patient that assertiveness involves acknowledging that their needs, desires and feelings are as valid as everyone else's.

• Emphasise how everyone has the right to have and express feelings, to choose how to spend their time, to change their mind and say 'No' or 'I don't know' and to make decisions and mistakes.

• Help the patient to clarify their own goals and values so that they only agree to do things that are important to them.

• Explain that everything they say 'Yes' to means saying 'No' to something else.

• Encourage them to be confident in their ability to say 'No'. They may agree to something to keep others happy, even if it is inconsistent with their personal values.

• Encourage the patient to acknowledge the feelings of someone who persistently ignores their wishes, but to state 'No' politely, or 'Thank you for asking me, but I'm afraid I'm not able to do it.' Explain that it might be better to not give any reasons because this suggests to the other person that they may still be persuaded to change their mind.

• Explain how avoiding conflict is not helpful, despite the discomfort conflict can cause. It conveys the message that the patient does not value himself or herself and thinks it is more important to keep other people happy.

• Encourage the patient to manage criticism in a balanced way and refuse to let themselves be labelled (or to label others). For example, they should say 'I didn't manage to get all the work done today,' rather than, 'I am incompetent.'

• Explain how important it is for the patient not to try to guess other people's feelings but to listen and acknowledge them before expressing their own wishes clearly.

Develop self-confidence

Having self-confidence affects how people feel, behave and think. Achievement and competence make people feel confident, which can be seen in their body posture and movements and facial expressions. When someone with depression withdraws, their problems often worsen because their confidence suffers.

• Explain how the patient's degree of self-confidence will affect how they think, feel and behave. Highlight how it can be situation-specific and that very few people feel confident all the time. Some people can 'fake it' or will avoid situations in which they feel out of their depth.

• Encourage the patient to notice how confident people appear and to practise it themselves, using their body posture, eye contact, smile, voice, gestures and movement.

• Remind the patient that being competent in achieving things will make them feel more confident. Encourage them to do things when they are stronger and not just when they are feeling vulnerable.

• Explain how boundaries are needed to define the nature of relationships. Being able to respect their own and other people's boundaries takes emotional maturity and boosts self-confidence. Emphasise that having poor boundaries can easily make other people come across as hurtful and controlling, and encourage them to notice whether a 'victim role' is a pattern for them.

• Explain that when depressed people withdraw and isolate themselves to avoid rejection and disappointment, that often makes their problem worse because their confidence will suffer.

• Encourage the patient to assess how reasonable their expectations are of their different relationships. Explain how most people are doing the best they can and no-one is perfect.

• Stimulate the patient to change the way they talk to themselves, from negative to neutral or positive. Suggest that they should talk to themselves as they would to other people, because generally this is a more balanced and supportive kind of talk.

• Encourage the patient to do things they enjoy with people who make them feel good. They do not need to change to suit others – it may be better to clarify their values and then find somewhere they fit in.

• Support the patient to be kind to themself. Encourage them not to blame anyone but instead acknowledge mistakes and let them go.

Case Study

Amanda's story

Amanda was in her early 40s and had young teenaged children. She had recently lost her mother after caring for her for several years. She visited her GP because she was feeling tearful and low in mood, sometimes feeling that life was not worth living. However, she expressed no intentions to harm herself.

What discussions with Amanda involved

- Discussing her current concerns, which included difficulties in asserting herself in her relationship with her partner.
- Acknowledging her losses both of her caring role and of her mother.
- Identifying that she used to enjoy walking, but had stopped because she felt tired.
- Discussing the effects of poor appetite and lack of sleep in making her low mood worse.
- Exploring the options for treatment, including antidepressants, counselling, GP support, and behavioural changes. She was not keen on taking medication but she was interested in seeing a counsellor.

Outcomes and changes for Amanda

Amanda underwent a few months of counselling and saw her GP on a regular basis. She started walking again with her friends and felt more motivated to prepare meals and eat more healthily. With help from her GP and her counsellor, she was able to say 'No' to unreasonable demands from her partner and other people and felt much more confident as a result. At one stage, when she was feeling particularly low, she decided jointly with her GP to start on a course of antidepressants to see if it would complement her behavioural and interpersonal approaches. She found the combined effects of this treatment helped her to move forward. Although she was still tired, she felt more in control and better supported by her friends and family.

Key points about Amanda's case

- This combined, flexible approach took the patient's wishes into account.
- Attention was paid to solving her current problems by building up her assertiveness skills.
- Acknowledgment was made of the stresses on her life situation, together with realistic goal setting.

- Ongoing support from her GP ensured her progress and changes were reviewed on a regular basis.
- Diet and exercise were used to promote feelings of well-being and encourage sleep.

Case Study

James's Story

James was in his late 20s and he had a young family. He had complained of a headache for nine months and was waiting to be referred to a second neurologist after being told there was nothing wrong by the first one he had seen. He came to the GP surgery for a well-man check and on questioning about his headache he explained it 'wasn't exactly a headache' and he wasn't really sure when he had it, but it was worrying him. He explained that he was helping out with child care during the night, driving long distances to work and sleeping poorly and that he felt exhausted. He felt that 'something had to give'.

What discussions with James involved

- Using open questions to ascertain that his real fear was about a brain tumour, partly because he had also lost his own father at a young age.
- Discussing how the headache was a constant source of worry for him and caused tension in his relationship with his wife.
- Encouraging him to think of it as 'pressure' rather than a headache, and using metaphors such as 'lifting a weight off his mind' to help think about the symptom as part of and a consequence of his current life situation.

Outcomes and changes for James

James was able to think differently about the headache in terms of representing something other than either a tumour or 'nothing', both of which were clearly unsatisfactory. He still had the opportunity to see another neurologist and to have further blood tests and other tests through the GP surgery. He was able to start making changes at home to improve both his relationships and his mood, without being labelled as depressed.

Key points about James' case

- The meaning and effects of his headache on his life were explored, regardless of the cause. It was useful to think about a metaphor for the headache so that it wasn't purely physical.

- He was asked what was different when the headache wasn't there, and this introduced the idea that it was not a constant thing, even if thinking and worrying about it were.
- The pressures of his life situation were 'normalised'. Marriage with two very young children, a long commute to work, and little shared time with his wife meant there were losses in both their social lives and their time alone.
- He was helped to understand that anxiety is made worse by tiredness. If he had a headache when he was carefree and full of energy it would probably have been hardly noticed.
- This was a problem-solving approach that viewed his difficulties as time-limited. He was offered hope that he and his wife could find solutions together.

Ideas for practice
- Ask a patient who believes they suffer from depression what it is that makes them vulnerable to feeling depressed. Try to use their responses to develop strategies to help prevent them from relapsing.
- Get the patient to notice when they are having repetitive negative thoughts. Then get them to imagine throwing the weight of their thoughts off their shoulders, or blowing away their clouds of thoughts, or simply clapping their hands together to break their 'trance-like' negative state.
- Encourage the patient to spend ten minutes a day sitting quietly and noticing their breathing. Each time their mind wanders, they should gently bring their focus back onto their breathing and notice how their body is feeling, and whether there are any areas of tension or heat or cold, for example.

Further reading

Butler, G. and Hope, T. (2009). *Manage Your Mind. The Mental Fitness Guide*. Oxford: Oxford University Press.

Crane, R. (2010). *Mindfulness-Based Cognitive Therapy*. Hove: Routledge.

David, L. (2010). *Using CBT in General Practice. The 10 Minute Consultation.* Oxfordshire. Scion Publishing.

Gilbert, P. (2009). *Overcoming Depression*, 3rd edn. London: Constable and Robinson.

Hamilton, D.R. (2010). *Why Kindness is Good for You.* London: Hay House.

Heaversedge, J. and Halliwell, E. (2010). *The Mindful Manifesto.* London: Hay House.

Mynors-Wallis, L., Moore, M., Maguire, J. and Hollingbery, T. (2004). *Shared Care in Mental Health.* New York: Oxford University Press.

Rai, G., Rosenthal, J., Morris, J. and Iliffe, S. (2006). *Shared Care of Older People.* Edinburgh: Elsevier.

Williams, M., Teasdale, J., Segal, Z. and Kabat-Zinn, J. (2007). *The Mindful Way Through Depression.* London: The Guilford Press.

Willson, R. and Branch, R. (2006). *Cognitive Behavioural Therapy for Dummies.* Chichester: John Wiley and Sons.

Yapko, M. (1997). *Breaking the Patterns of Depression.* New York: Broadway Books.

Yapko, M. (2009). *Depression is Contagious.* New York: Free Press.

CHAPTER 6
Managing anxiety

In this chapter you will learn how to manage the patient with anxiety, with regard to self-help and bibliotherapy, encouraging relaxation and a sense of control, challenging unhelpful ways of thinking, and promoting distraction and mindfulness. It also explains how to identify avoidance behaviour, and – very importantly – why you should remember yourself in these situations. Further case studies are used illustrate the management of anxiety.

A feeling of fear or anxiety is a common experience that affects everyone from time to time. It is a natural response to a perceived threat and as such it serves a vital function in keeping us safe. A sense of anxiety may be caused by a change in a person's social or material circumstances and may be a useful – if uncomfortable – signal that things need to change. For example, there may be a situation or relationship that is harmful to their well-being or signs of physical symptoms that need investigation. However, the natural anxiety response can also become exaggerated and prolonged in a way that causes stress and illness. This probably occurs in around one in ten of the population at any time. The initial feeling of fear triggers certain patterns of thinking and behaviour that can become problematic.

Unhelpful and chronic anxiety may be defined as marked feelings of fear, worry and apprehension in excess of any potential threat (Mynors-Wallis *et al.*, 2004), which in healthcare may alter help-seeking behaviour and become a source of frustration for both professionals and patients alike. The 'anxiety balance' is important (Williams, 2003) because not only is the danger or threat exaggerated in the person's mind, but also the perceived ability to cope is underestimated. This causes oversensitivity to potential threats and attempts to avoid them. In other words, it is not the problem or situation alone that causes the anxiety or worry, but rather how it is interpreted. In people with anxiety, the response to any difficulties is to worry, which is not in itself an effective solution. It is actually a form of avoidance. People who are worrying are not likely to be focusing on finding solutions. Instead they will be ruminating on repetitive thoughts and imagining increasingly catastrophic outcomes. Someone who is feeling chronically anxious may also be drinking excessive amounts of alcohol, taking drugs, smoking or over-eating to try to relieve their distressing feelings. Because such behaviours do not effectively relieve the symptoms – and often make them worse – this causes more anxiety and fuels the cycle of worrying without addressing the underlying problems.

Anxiety can occur with long-term physical illness and may be related to fears about the future or about changes in functioning. Patients may no longer be able to work or may withdraw from pleasurable activities, with the effect that life seems more mundane and frustrating. Patients may also have a general 'health anxiety', seeing doctors with a range of symptoms such as sleep disturbances, asthma, angina, skin conditions, irritable bowel syndrome, peptic ulcers and other physical complaints. It is necessary in such cases to rule out serious illness, but over-investigation and attention to the physical problems can make the anxiety worse and increase the risk of further somatisation. Reassurance is usually counter-productive and patients will turn to other practitioners for a second opinion as they become hypervigilant and focus almost exclusively on their physical sensations.

> It is important to be aware of the difference between anxiety and agitated depression, which is a high risk for suicide. Anxiety is generally a lifelong habit or tendency, not something that suddenly appears later in life, whereas this kind of agitation may occur in someone who was previously depressed (or has recently developed depression) and may be triggered by a specific event.

HOW TO

Manage anxiety

For more about the techniques and principles described below, see the Further Reading section at the back of this chapter.

Encourage relaxation

You may have to deal with an anxious, distressed, angry or agitated patient, where the emphasis is on helping them to relax enough to be receptive to you and know you are listening and understand them fully.

- Engage effectively with a distressed or anxious patient using your skills to quickly establish rapport and help them feel more relaxed.

- Remember that an anxious patient will find your information irrelevant unless they first feel heard and understood.

- Aim to relax your patient and yourself so you can address the pertinent issues and consider possibilities with less emotional interference.

- Try to match the 'emotional tempo' of the patient who is particularly angry or agitated. For example, use a voice more like theirs to reflect that you understand their heightened feelings. Make eye contact and turn partially or directly towards them in an open way.

- Try to find out what is bothering the patient most. Use careful questioning to clarify their concerns. This will convey that you are really listening and want to understand what they are saying, and it will make subsequent planning of care and treatment more relevant.

Promote a sense of control

Promoting a sense of control for the anxious patient involves helping them to manage their responses, recognising their overall ability to cope, and helping them identify which anxiety-provoking issues can be reduced or eliminated.

Explain how the physiological fight or flight response is the same as that of our ancestors, who depended on it for their survival. We just need to understand and manage these responses differently nowadays.

- Help the patient realise they may be more prone to feeling anxious in some situations than others. Ask what makes them vulnerable to anxiety. Is it tiredness, hunger, the presence of certain other people, or certain situations?

- Find ways to separate the patient's 'anxiety' from who they are. Ask how anxiety creeps up on them and what that anxiety makes them do.

- Set the patient a task to interrupt the 'normal' pattern of events. For example, ask them to keep track of what they do during the following week that helps them feel more in control of things.

- Explain how intolerance of uncertainty is a major issue for most people who worry. Anxiety makes people search for guarantees and can lead to repeated demands for reassurance.

- Try to maintain rapport and explore their concerns with them. Acknowledge that uncertainty is inevitable and can usually be tolerated.

- Help the patient realise they can handle difficulties by asking about things they have coped with in the past, or point out that they are currently managing to function in their lives.

- Reassure the patient that it is possible to modify the effects of anxiety by changing their habits of thinking and behaviour.

- Explain that the anxiety does not need to be eliminated. It may be a sign that things need to change. If it is excessive and debilitating, aim to lower its intensity and suggest that they could 'turn down the dial' or 'reduce its volume'.

- Establish whether the anxiety is a signal that something needs to change. If it is, then there will be definite questions that need addressing, and a problem-solving approach should be taken. Problem-solving means addressing the things that can be altered and distinguishing them from those that cannot. Encourage the patient to let go of what is uncontrollable, and focus on any immediate problems.

- Suggest that the patient writes down any worries that arise, when they arise, and schedules in a time to think about them. Acting on them this way can reduce the negative effect of their 'rumination'.

Challenge unhelpful ways of thinking

Creating extreme and negative explanations for events is a common way of thinking in people with anxiety. The thoughts can occur very rapidly and can be unquestioned if the patient feels and acts as if they were true.

These automatic, negative ways of viewing things often involve distorted thinking, inappropriate expectations and personalisation of situations, and catastrophising.

• Aim to notice and question any extreme statements that the patient makes, and introduce doubt into any expressed certainties.

• Encourage the patient to dispute their beliefs and to examine the evidence for them.

• Encourage the patient to consider as many alternative explanations for events as they can to challenge their automatic, negative way of viewing things.

• State emphatically that other explanations for events are possible. Even if the patient finds this hard to believe, they cannot deny that an alternative explanation may be true.

• Explain to a patient who repeatedly searches for certainty that there is nothing seriously wrong with them that full guarantees are never possible. There is a chance that their feared outcome *may* happen. Repeating the outcome they fear to themself ('… I may get cancer … I may get cancer …') can be helpful for these patients, and although their level of anxiety may increase initially, the thought will at some point stop being fearful and become neutral and boring. (This strategy depends on the context – patients who are overwhelmed with anxiety about a condition because their friend died of it, for example, are very unlikely to have the same problem, so you might tell them that their worst fears are very unlikely to be true.)

• Look for other types of distorted thinking, such as catastrophising or worrying about one event leading to another that will eventually turn into a catastrophe. The patient may habitually do this when it would be better maintain focus on the precipitating event.

• Ask the patient what is the immediate issue or problem that needs to be solved. It is impossible to address something that has not happened and it is unlikely that things will deteriorate in the way that an anxious patient fears.

• Remind the patient, in a good way, that all of us are fairly insignificant in the wider scheme of things. Personalising situations, or assuming everything is about oneself and bearing all the responsibility for events are common themes in people with chronic anxiety. Suggest that most people are too worried about themselves to think much about anyone else. In one patient's words: 'I have always been anxious. Always worried about everything. And then one day I just realised, it's not all about you, Pete!'

• Ask the patient to think about what would or would not satisfy them in a particular situation or relationship. They may begin to realise that their expectations are the problem rather than the situation itself. People who are prone to anxiety may have unhelpfully high standards and inappropriate expectations of other people or certain situations. They often feel a failure or let down by other people, which leads to more frustration and a risk of depression.

• Encourage the patient to distinguish productive from unproductive worry, to deal with the unproductive worry in another way and change the productive worry into active problem-solving. Differentiate between productive and unproductive worry or 'rumination' by asking the patient what would serve as an answer to their worrying thought and what action they should be taking. If no immediate action can be taken, then that worry can be categorised as unproductive.

Teach distraction and mindfulness

One way of distracting the patient from anxious thoughts is through mindfulness. Mindfulness involves simply observing what is going on rather than thinking about what is going on. The patient must 'mindfully' pay attention to real things, instead of 'mindlessly' getting lost in their own thoughts.

• Explain that being able to relax or calm one's self at vital moments is a valuable skill for anyone suffering with anxiety, both for relieving distressing feelings and for enabling a rational assessment of events.

• Describe how being mindful can help to foster an attitude of acceptance by simply observing what is going on, rather than particularly thinking about it. This means having an awareness of what is happening and paying attention to real things, rather than being 'mindlessly' lost in thoughts and functioning on automatic pilot.

• Encourage the patient to cultivate mindfulness by choosing to notice sounds or smells or looking around at things, literally looking upwards and outwards or making more eye contact with people, rather than looking down and focusing inward on their thoughts.

• Explain the most common technique of focusing on breathing, and the nature of the in-and out-breaths. These are useful because they our breaths are always with us, and there are lots of different exercises. The patient could notice the breath without trying to change it or modify it. Or they could make the out-breath last longer than the in-breath, perhaps breathing in to a count of seven and out to a count of eleven. Another breathing technique that has the same relaxing effect is breathing in for four seconds and holding for four, then breathing out for four and holding for four.

• Describe other techniques that harness the natural relaxation response, such as fist clenching or whole-body relaxation. These involve deliberately tensing muscles throughout the body and then noticing the feeling of relaxation as they are released.

• Suggest that the patient imagines a safe and special place to help them relax. If the patient dislikes the idea of being 'calm' then get them to imagine doing a strenuous physical activity such as swimming or skiing.

• Explain that learning these skills to manage anxiety will take practice and repetition. It is important to convey a sense that change is possible.

• Make sure that the patient challenges any unhelpful thoughts and distorted perceptions. Being distracted from anxious thoughts will help, but is not the whole solution, and it may encourage a habit of avoidance.

Identify avoidance behaviour

Avoidance behaviour is often displayed by people with anxiety as they try to limit exposure to difficult situations or feelings. However this gives only a short-term reduction in anxiety and may lead to the development of further complications. It is useful to pinpoint which challenging people or situations the patient tends to avoid.

• Explain to the patient that anyone who worries will be avoiding doing or thinking about many things or anxiety-provoking situations, people or places. This may be quite subtle, not even obvious to the patient, and may involve avoiding eye contact or cutting off a conversation that makes the patient feel anxious.

• Explain how this kind of avoidance may initially reduce anxiety, but it makes things worse in the longer term, because the behaviour reinforces the belief that avoiding a difficult situation is the only way to deal with it.

• Explain how avoidance reduces the patient's opportunities to find out that their worst fears are unlikely to happen, which means the anxiety increases and self-confidence suffers. These opportunities may be potentially life-enhancing, offering new connections, relationships and enjoyable activities. Their loss will increase both anxiety and the risk of depression.

• Ask the patient about avoiding difficult situations, whether there is anything they will not do or anywhere they will not go because of their anxiety. Are there people they avoid? What would they do differently if they were not feeling anxious? Do they tend to choose the easiest option when making decisions?

• Ask the patient about behaviours they use to comfort themselves when they feel bad. Some patients' anxiety is obvious, but others control their symptoms by avoiding difficult situations, masking their feelings with alcohol or other substances, or engaging in compulsive rituals.

• Take a step-by-step problem-solving approach to help the patient overcome avoidance. In anxiety it must be planned and steady, not attempting too much too quickly. Identify short, medium and long-term targets if appropriate.

• Help the patient to identify the problem or area of avoidance to be tackled and then get them to think of possible solutions. Assess the advantages and disadvantages of each. The patient should choose a solution, plan the necessary steps to reach the goal, carry out the plan and review its outcome.

Self-help or bibliotherapy

Self-help books are a common source of support for people in distress and there are schemes around the country that aim to recommend or 'prescribe' appropriate books for patients, either by trained mental health staff or generalists such as GPs and practice nurses. Recent research by Scanlan (2010) suggests that overall the benefits of self-help books are significant, despite some negative experiences relating to obtaining the books or poor-quality follow-up from the healthcare practitioner who prescribed the book. The patient may find 'meaningful resonance' through this kind of reading, whereby they can identify with written accounts and advice in a way that comforts them. They often feel well in comparison with the people they read about, and feel reassured by shared experience when they realise they are not alone in feeling this way, and they often feel more hopeful and therefore more motivated to make positive changes themselves.

The research suggested that the patient should be encouraged to find and read books in a 'normal' way. There should no perception of stigma, of being 'prescribed' a book as part of a special scheme that singles them out as having mental health problems, just the knowledge that they have the support and guidance of appropriately trained and knowledgeable practitioners. The quality of the relationship between the clinician and the patient was found to make a difference to the outcome. Patients had more positive experiences when they had good engagement and did not feel hurried during consultations. The aims of self-help, whether part of a wider treatment strategy or not, should be two-fold – to engage with the instructional aspect of the book (usually CBT) and to identify with the stories and accounts of other people they describe, in order to engender a sense of hope and optimism for recovery (Scanlan, 2010). Poetry and fiction also have a role in helping people find meaning and think differently about their own situations.

Remember yourself

Caring professionals can easily get drawn in to other people's anxieties and feel responsible for finding solutions to their problems. We therefore need to be aware of our own pressures, both from our personal lives and the demands of work. We need to notice our own emotions, thoughts and behaviour, including prejudices, and take heed of any early warning signs that indicate a need for rest or recuperation. We are more prone to absorb other people's distress and anxiety when we are tired, or low or overwhelmed with other stresses ourselves. Pressure of all sorts comes not only from external sources, but also from within as we strive to achieve and meet our personal expectations. We should identify our own triggers and any poor coping strategies that may need replacing with more positive behaviour and activities.

Case Study

Marion's story

Marion was 51 years old and had been taking time off work because of stress, while awaiting a referral to a counsellor. She needed an extension to her period of sick leave, because she was tearful and having panic attacks and felt unable to return to work.

What discussions with Marion involved

- Exploring the timeline and triggers for her problems. Although she was an experienced and well-regarded team leader, she was being bullied by her new boss.
- Asking whether she always tended to be anxious about things or whether this was unusual for her. She did tend to worry but this matter was much worse.
- Explaining how the surge of adrenaline in the fight or flight response can cause the physical sensation of panic, but this can be altered by thinking differently about trigger situations.
- Suggesting that her bullying boss may be threatened by her skills, and talking about ways to meet some of his needs for control and competence without compromising her own.
- Explaining how avoidance would fuel her anxiety further, and rehearsing ways for her to assert her own needs without angry outbursts that might be perceived as aggressive.
- Emphasising that the needs of both herself and her boss were equally important and encouraging awareness of how her reactions may be misinterpreted.

Outcomes and changes for Marion

Marion was immediately more relaxed after the discussion. A few days later she reported to a colleague that she had found it very helpful and felt ninety per cent better. She still intended taking up the referral for counselling and hoped shortly to return to work.

Key points about Marion's case

- There was a very specific focus on her key problems. Although Marion had a tendency to be a bit anxious, this episode was triggered off by a particular relationship at work.
- The relationship was reframed and viewed as a bullying situation in which her boss probably felt undermined by her skills and reputation.
- Her physical symptoms were described in terms of a stress response.
- She was given the belief that the situation was manageable, with a focus on changing her ways of thinking and rehearsing her responses. Her awareness was raised of how altering her behaviour could alter his behaviour.
- A self-help book was recommended that had particular relevance to her situation and offered her an opportunity to explore things further using her own resources.
- She was given support from other members of the healthcare team, including a counsellor.

Case Study

Janice's story

When Janice was in her late 50s, she lost a friend to breast cancer and began having panic attacks, even when the word cancer was mentioned. She had to leave work, attending the GP surgery frequently with concerns about her health.

What discussions with Janice involved

- Explaining that anxiety her anxiety was a normal response to the loss of someone she cared about and with whom she closely identified.
- Discussing her past experiences of anxiety. She said she had become more anxious since reaching the menopause.
- Explaining the physiology of panic attacks and the fight or flight reaction.
- Describing how accepting uncertainty was central to managing her current anxiety because anyone may develop cancer or any other condition, but she would be able to deal with such things if they arose.

Outcomes and changes for Janice

Janice looked relaxed and smiled a lot as her issues were discussed, and she acknowledged that she would be able to cope with the uncertainty that was a normal part of life. She agreed and understood anyway that no test was one hundred per cent accurate in identifying disease and that searching for reassurance in this way only made her feel worse.

Key points about Janice's case

- It set her current problem in the context of bereavement.
- An understanding and respectful approach was taken with respect to her difficulties.
- She was given an explanation of anxiety and the probable link with her hormonal changes.
- Coping strategies for use in difficult situations were discussed.
- The situation was 'normalised' and she was given a sense that her problem was solvable.

Ideas for practice

- Ask the patient what makes them vulnerable to anxiety. For example, do they feel more anxious when they are tired? Or when they are in a specific situation?
- Encourage the patient to imagine turning down a dial to lower the intensity of their anxiety. Watch their responses as they imagine their anxiety reducing.
- Discuss how anxiety makes people seek certainty in a way that is not realistic. Ask them to think about how they have handled more difficult things in the past and then suggest that they will be able to manage any challenges they may face in the future.

Further reading

Butler, G. and Hope, T. (2009). *Manage Your Mind. The Mental Fitness Guide.* Oxford: Oxford University Press.

David, L. (2010). *Using CBT in General Practice. The 10 Minute Consultation.* Oxfordshire. Scion Publishing.

Leahy, R.L. (2010). *The Worry Cure.* London: Piatkus.

Mynors-Wallis, L., Moore, M., Maguire, J. and Hollingbery, T. (2004). *Shared Care in Mental Health*. New York: Oxford University Press.

Williams, M., Teasdale, J., Segal, Z. and Kabat-Zinn, J. (2007). *The Mindful Way Through Depression*. London: The Guilford Press.

Willson, R. and Branch, R. (2006). *Cognitive Behavioural Therapy for Dummies*. Chichester: John Wiley and Sons.

CHAPTER 7

Promoting behaviour change

This chapter explores the concept of changing health-related behaviour, by addressing patients' level of awareness, by working with them to make plans and set goals, whilst anticipating high-risk situations. The main principles discussed in the chapter are illustrated by two relevant case studies.

People go through many different changes throughout their lives and only rarely need intervention or treatment from healthcare professionals. This natural process of change can be harnessed to improve health-related behaviour if we understand how it works. For many healthcare professionals, achieving lasting changes through behavioural interventions can seem to be quite rare, but when it does occur it is very rewarding and can save a lot of money for the health service.

Motivational interviewing (MI) involves conversations about behaviour, initially developed in (but by no means limited to) situations of problem drinking and chronic disease, whereby the practitioner becomes more effective and acts as a catalyst in the change process. People can readily modify their behaviour if they resolve their ambivalence about wanting to do so. Motivation is not a fixed entity but something that varies according to circumstances and it comprises readiness, ability and willingness to change (Miller and Rollnick, 2002). For example, someone may feel capable of changing and believe it is important to do so, but they may lack

the motivation to change because they have other priorities at that time. As a healthcare professional, it is easy to assume that the patient's health is their main concern – that they ought to change and it is a professional failure if they don't. However, patients have complex and competing priorities, and our role is to guide them towards their goals by making sense of their feelings. In MI the concept of *discrepancy* is used to describe the difference between where the person is now and where they want to be. If in their mind their current behaviour fits with their goals and values they will see no reason to change. If however they view their current situation differently and find it inconsistent with their broader values, then the increase in discrepancy between their behaviour and their goals makes change more likely to occur.

Increasingly in modern society we see a dependence on substances to fulfil emotional needs, hence the use of alcohol, tobacco, food, and prescribed or non-prescribed drugs. Helman (2007) describes how the comfort gained from these substances is part of a wider belief that we just need to 'take something' to make ourselves feel better. Believing this idea means that the underlying problems are not addressed, and continuing the behaviour reinforces the feeling that it works. People may ingest substances either for their influence on mood, such as a loss of inhibition with alcohol, or to stave off the effects of withdrawal. The effects can be as much psychological as physical, often having less to do with the substance properties than how the person expects to feel after taking it. Expecting the substance to induce a particular feeling becomes a self-fulfilling prophecy. The role of expectation is critical in behaviour change.

Social factors are important in determining which substances are available or culturally acceptable, and how likely it is that a change will be made in their use. It may help to explore the 'symbolic' meaning of the behaviour, whether it represents a way to conform and feel part of a social unit or whether it is an act of rebellion against family or some cultural group. Whether someone happens to smoke, drink too much alcohol, or over-eat is almost irrelevant; the meaning of the behaviour will differ both between people and within an individual depending on their mood. For example, drinking in a social setting may serve a different purpose to drinking alone after a difficult day at work. Exploring the pattern and meaning of this behaviour with an attitude of openness and curiosity will help the patient assess their current situation more objectively.

HOW TO

Help change behaviour

For more about the techniques and principles described below, see the Further Reading section at the back of this chapter.

Increase awareness

This focuses on teaching the patient to be aware of their automatic behaviours, triggers and habits to foster objective attitudes and allow them to acquire new habits. Many of these behaviours involve the use of some substance that alters the patient's emotional, mental or physical state, such as food or alcohol.

• Describe how automatic behaviours occur as if the patient is in a trance. This allows patients to identify with the feeling and begin to view the habit more objectively.

• Discuss the patient's patterns of behaviours, including trigger situations, and emphasise that they are just habits which can be dropped and replaced by new ones.

• Emphasise how the patient can alter the future by making changes now. Relate the consequences specifically to particular problems, such as diabetes, high blood pressure or abnormal liver tests. Be aware that a patient with a new diagnosis or worsening symptoms may be open to suggestions because the effects of the behaviour are apparent (however, this cannot be assumed).

• Try to introduce doubt regarding the anticipated effects of the substance or food. Explain how nicotine is a stimulant that increases anxiety and alcohol is a depressant that lowers mood.

• Explain that having two days a week without alcohol and not consuming all the week's allowable units in a few days will be good for their liver. Mention how tolerance to alcohol can develop, and that not feeling drunk may be a bad sign because it means they are at greater risk of harm due to consuming more.

• Encourage them to notice their emotional, mental and physical state when they engage in the behaviour. They might keep a diary to record their consumption of food or alcohol or how many cigarettes they smoke, as well as the circumstances they do it in, and how they feel at the time they eat, or smoke or drink.

• Notice whether they think that there are health risks for other people but not themselves. They might say 'There's no cancer in the family,' or 'I don't drink that much.' If so, respect their viewpoint but offer an alternative perspective.

- Ask how smoking gets 'a hold' of them, how alcohol makes them do things they don't want to do, or what makes them eat more than they planned. Talk about what the substance does to them in terms of behaviour and effects.

- Explore the symbolic meaning that may be attached to the behaviour, either now or in the past. Perhaps the pint of beer or cigarette represents being sociable, or they over-eat because they were punished as a child for not finishing meals.

- Ask them if they eat for reasons other than hunger, for example when they are actually thirsty, or they are fed up or tired.

Explore motivation

Motivation can be explored using reflective listening and open questioning techniques, in order to determine the patient's goals and values and narrow the gap between where they are now and where they want to be in the future.

- Use reflective listening, by paraphrasing what you think the patient has said to you, to discuss some of the pros and cons of making changes. Understand what they perceive as benefits of the behaviour before discussing the costs.

- Use open questions to let the patient find their own solutions. Ask what concerns them most about their behaviour, what keeps them smoking, drinking or over-eating and how their behaviour affects other people.

- Try to discover the patient's larger goals and values. Engage their imagination to visualise how their future will differ if they either continue or change the habit.

- Try to increase their perception of discrepancy between their current behaviour and their stated goals or values.

- Ask them how important these changes are to them, how confident they feel that they could carry them out, and how much of a priority they are for them at the moment.

- If not a priority at that time, find out what the patient is ready to do. Ask which one thing they would like to change.

- Use a scale to rate the patient's current levels of confidence and importance. If the scores are low, then ask what would make them higher. Very low scores suggest they are not yet ready to make changes, so reflect back your perception of the situation and leave the door open for future conversations.

• Find new ways to think about the problem, such as, 'You are looking after your children's health but what about you?' or 'You forget to take your insulin when you get home, but you remember to have a drink … I am confident that you can remember the insulin as well!'

• Ask if there are any barriers to change, such as other people or current difficulties, and help the patient plan ways to manage them.

Make plans and set goals

This is about making plans and setting goals, not in isolation, but together with helping the patient identify their support network, to make significant people in their life aware of their intentions, and to focus their attention on how their life will be different when their goals are achieved.

• Ask the patient if you were to ring one person there and then to support them, who would that be?

• Do not make all the suggestions for plans and goals yourself. Instead ask what they think would work for them. When they would be most likely to fit in a walk, for example, or what could they do differently?

• Identify the steps towards their goal, while acknowledging that there may be some discomfort or frustration along the way.

• Focus on maintaining behavioural changes rather than measuring outcomes, particularly with respect to losing weight which takes time to reach a target.

• Rehearse success by asking the patient to describe how they will look and behave when they have changed their habit and how other people will respond differently to them.

• Remind them how the instant gratification of indulging in the behaviour is short-lived and can be replaced by the satisfaction of having more control over their actions.

• Explain that keeping track of something they do automatically may be stressful and it may even increase the behaviour in the short term, but this stage will pass.

• Encourage even small changes in behaviour. By repeatedly doing new things, the patient will gain confidence and make further progress.

• Share stories about other people who have made changes in similar circumstances. Patients may identify with them and imagine being successful themselves.

- Discuss the patient's triggers for their behaviour. They may be vulnerable when they are bored, lonely or tired and need to think about meeting these needs in other ways. Making other lifestyle changes at the same time can help if the focus is on a new healthy way of life, rather than just removing something they used to enjoy.

- Discuss the potential impact of behaviour change on other people. They may need to have responses ready to help maintain their resolve.

Plan strategies for high-risk situations

High-risk situations may involve certain triggers like specific places, or feelings such as boredom or low mood. The patient can be helped to notice, avoid or face situations that arise and to appreciate when they deal with them successfully.

- Encourage the patient to recognise what presents as a high risk for them and plan how to avoid or deal with those situations, for example by seeing different people or getting more rest to prevent tiredness.

- Explain that it is normal to go through a relapsing course when changing behaviour and reframe relapse as a 'blip' that does not detract from their larger goal. They can use it to learn how to cope with similar situations.

- Suggest that they enlist the support of others, but they must state clearly what kind of help they want and when they want it.

- Suggest they make a list of reasons to remind them of the importance of changing.

- Encourage them to think about how they successfully managed to change previously, or how they could have managed a relapse differently last time.

- Explain how the urge to perform the habit may be very strong at times but is often short-lived. Help them to identify suitable distractions or to remind themselves that any discomfort will pass.

- Encourage them to notice if they are performing patterns from the early stages of the behaviour and help them to develop a 'stop strategy' when they do.

- Encourage them to reward themselves for their success if they think it will help. Remember that genuine reflected praise from you will always be welcome!

Case Study

Sara's story

Sara was 32 years old when her blood pressure readings were found to be raised on three separate occasions. She was very overweight with a high body mass index and was categorised as obese, but she was otherwise well. She had previous experience of dieting and was able to lose several kilograms, but always put it back on again. She made sure her children ate well so that they maintained a healthy weight.

What discussions with Sara involved

- Talking about the relationship between weight and blood pressure.
- Explaining that she would need to consider either lifestyle changes or medication to reduce the health risks, and asking her what she preferred.
- Asking about her previous experiences of losing weight.
- Reflecting that she did a great job of looking after other people and clearly knew how to eat healthily, and adding 'But what about you?'
- Asking her how she thought she could fit some exercise into her daily routine.

Outcomes and changes for Sara

Her blood pressure was back in the normal range within two months and after four months later she had lost about 20 kilograms in weight, was walking and swimming regularly and no longer felt out of breath when walking uphill. She realised that being scolded as a child for not finishing her meals meant she had stopped noticing if she was hungry, which she had now been able to change.

Key points about Sara's case

- The trigger was a situation of raised blood pressure with potential health risks and the possibility of needing life-long medication.
- She was able to decide how she wanted to get her blood pressure back to normal.
- Her current situation was reframed and reflected to allow Sara to focus on her own needs.
- Questions were used that allowed her to make decisions rather than giving direct advice.
- This was a supportive relationship with regular reviews to discuss and monitor her progress.

Case Study

David's story

David was in his early 60s. He had type 2 diabetes and was on insulin therapy. His weight had increased steadily to a body mass index of 42 which is categorised as obese. His blood glucose control was poor and he was at risk of developing diabetic complications.

What discussions with David involved

- Discussing his latest weight and blood-glucose results.
- Asking if he would like to lose weight and getting him to list his reasons.
- Looking at his weight over time and using a computer to plot a graph. This revealed excellent weight loss a few years ago. When asked what had happened at that time, he recalled walking his dog regularly. The dog had since died.
- Encouraging him by acknowledging that he was extremely successful at losing weight when he put his mind to it.
- Discussing together ways he thought he could lose weight at this time, and forming a suitable plan.

Outcomes and changes for David

Six months later he had lost 12 kilograms in weight. He had done this by walking the neighbour's dog every day and reducing the size of his food portions. His blood glucose level was also improved and he was able to reduce the amount of insulin needed for treatment.

Key points about David's case

- The principle was an affirmation that he was someone who could succeed. Highlighting and then building on his existing strengths made him realise he could make the necessary changes.
- He was asked to provide his own reasons for losing weight rather than dictating reasons to him.
- The management plan was formulated using his ideas – not anyone else's.
- Open questions were used well, such as 'How could you lose weight?'
- At the end of the consultation, what had been planned was summarised and a timescale for review was agreed.

Case Study

John's story

John also had type 2 diabetes. He was 57 years old and worked in a sedentary professional job that involved many meals out entertaining clients. His blood glucose control was deteriorating, and his risk of developing diabetic complications was increasing. He was unwilling to consider starting insulin treatment.

What discussions with John involved

- Exploring his feelings regarding insulin and his ability to sustain a healthy weight loss.
- Expressing genuine concern that his health would be at risk if his blood glucose control did not improve significantly over the next year.
- Explaining that he was one of a small number of patients with high blood glucose chosen for special attention from the GP.
- Assuring him that he could come back for appointments as often as he found helpful.
- Encouraging him to formulate a plan of his own, that involved regular gym visits, reducing alcohol intake, eating very healthy food at home, and 'damage limitation' when entertaining clients.

Outcomes and changes for John

One year later, John was delighted to have lost about 10 kilograms and his blood glucose levels were much improved. He appreciated being one of his GP's 'special' group of patients, and was reassured to know that he could visit her any time he wanted (although he did not feel the need to do this).

Key points about John's case

- Open questions were used to allow him to think about his situation clearly.
- He was given the choice of how he could get his diabetes under control and he formulated a plan with support from the clinician.
- His decision regarding insulin was respected and the onus for making changes in other ways was put onto him.
- He was given affirmation, emphasising that he could succeed.
- He knew his diabetes control was important to both him and his doctor.

- His plan was realistic and took into account his current lifestyle and the demands and expectations of his job.
- He was made to feel special, which meant a lot and was a big motivation for him.

Ideas for practice

- Ask the patient to rate how important it is for them to change their current behaviour and how confident they feel. What would it take to increase their confidence?
- Ask the patient about any previous attempts at changing their behaviour. Reframe what seemed like a failed attempt to make changes as evidence that they know what to do, but just need to manage their relapses better. Draw parallels between stopping one behaviour successfully and the current one.
- Ask whether this change is a priority for them at the moment. If it is not, then explore other things they would like to change first.

Further reading

Butler, G. and Hope, T. (2009). *Manage Your Mind. The Mental Fitness Guide.* Oxford: Oxford University Press.

David, L. (2010). *Using CBT in General Practice. The 10 Minute Consultation.* Oxfordshire. Scion Publishing.

Miller, W.R. and Rollnick, S. (2002). *Motivational Interviewing. Preparing People for Change,* 2nd edn. London: The Guilford Press.

Mynors–Wallis, L., Moore, M., Maguire, J. and Hollingbery, T. (2004). *Shared Care in Mental Health.* New York: Oxford University Press.

Rollnick, S., Miller, W.R. and Butler, C.C. (2008). *Motivational Interviewing in Health Care. Helping Patients Change Behaviour.* New York: The Guilford Press.

Willson, R. and Branch, R. (2006). *Cognitive Behavioural Therapy for Dummies.* Chichester: John Wiley and Sons.

CHAPTER 8
Concluding Comments

The general perception that medicine is scientific rather than psychological presents us with a number of professional and organisational challenges. The whole person who comes to a healthcare consultation may not have a discrete physical disease that needs to be treated with medication. A reductionist approach to medicine can be vital at times, but it often risks conveying a false sense of certainty that does not reflect the complexity of the patient's presenting problems. As an alternative to looking inwards and fragmenting the picture we can attend instead to the patient's story that describes their experience of illness. The story will often provide the clues we need to make sense of what is happening to them. It is also likely to offer the beginnings of the solution in which their personal resources, social support, health beliefs and values all play a part.

As healthcare professionals we should be able to convey a sense that everyone is prone to difficulties and that an individual patient's responses are simply part of a normal spectrum of behaviour. We should include ourselves, because none of us is immune to problems or suffering; for most of us, building up confidence about this takes time, as does the inclination to examine ourselves more critically. It does not mean inappropriately sharing information or making our needs the focus of the consultation. Instead it means developing an understanding of the threads that are common to all human behaviours and experience. It is possible to convey genuine empathy towards the patient while maintaining boundaries that protect both parties in a functional and therapeutic relationship.

Whatever degree of psychological skills and empathy, language ability and observational skills we have, we can always improve. What is most important is our attitude towards our patients and our willingness to put them at the centre of the healthcare process. If we can address patients' needs holistically, we are likely to improve disease outcomes, reduce distress and increase their sense of control. A conversation with patients that leads to greater understanding of their treatment options is likely to reduce waste and limit iatrogenic illness. The demands on healthcare are rising as technology develops, expectations increase and what we consider as 'health' gets broader. We will need to combine our physical and psychological skills to make better use of limited resources. In the end, we matter as much as the techniques we use, and the practitioner–patient relationship matters the most. Our expectations and interest in our patients are at the core of the healing process, where *attention* is perhaps the most effective drug we have to offer.

References

Asen, E., Tomson, D., Young, V. and Tomson, P. (2009). *Ten Minutes for the Family. Systemic Interventions in Primary Care.* London: Routledge.

Balint, M. (2000). *The Doctor, His Patient and the Illness: Millennium Edition.* Edinburgh: Churchill Livingstone (original edition 1957).

Boardman, J., Henshaw, C. and Willmott, S. (2004). Needs for mental health treatment among general practice attenders. *British Journal of Psychiatry* 185, 318–27.

Butler, G. and Hope, T. (2009). *Manage Your Mind. The Mental Fitness Guide.* Oxford: Oxford University Press.

Crane, R. (2010). *Mindfulness-Based Cognitive Therapy.* Hove: Routledge.

David, L. (2010). *Using CBT in General Practice. The 10 Minute Consultation.* Oxfordshire: Scion Publishing.

Department of Health (1996). *NHS Executive Report. Burdens of Disease.* Leeds: Department of Health.

Gilbert, P. (2009). *Overcoming Depression,* 3rd edn. London: Constable and Robinson.

Greenberg, T.M. (2007). *The Psychological Impact of Acute and Chronic Illness. A Practical Guide for Primary Care Physicians.* New York: Springer.

Griffin, J. and Tyrrell, L. (2004). *Human Givens. A New Approach to Emotional Health and Clear Thinking.* Chalvington: Human Givens.

Griffin, J. and Tyrrell, I. (2006). *Dreaming Reality. How Dreaming Keeps Us Sane or Can Drive Us Mad.* Chalvington: Human Givens.

Grinder, M. (2009). *Charisma. The Art of Relationships.* Battle Ground, WA: Michael Grinder and Associates.

Heaversedge, J. and Halliwell, E. (2010). *The Mindful Manifesto.* London: Hay House.

Helman, C.G. (2006). *Suburban Shaman. Tales From Medicine's Frontline.* London: Hammersmith Press.

Helman, C.G. (2007). *Culture, Health and Illness,* 5th edn. London: Hodder Arnold.

Kurtz, S. and Silverman, J. (1996). The Calgary–Cambridge observation guides. An aid to defining the curriculum and organising the teaching in communication training programmes. *Medical Education* 30, 83–89.

Leahy, R.L. (2010). *The Worry Cure.* London: Piatkus.

Macdonald, A. (2008). *Solution-Focused Therapy. Theory, Research and Practice.* London: Sage Publications.

Meltzer, H., Gill, B. and Petticrew, M. (1995). *OPCS surveys of psychiatric morbidity in Great Britain. Report No. 1. The presence of psychiatric morbidity amongst adults aged 16 to 64 living in private households in Great Britain.* London: HMSO.

Miller, W.R. and Rollnick, S. (2002). *Motivational Interviewing. Preparing People for Change,* 2nd edn. London: The Guilford Press.

Molden, D. and Hutchinson, P. (2006). *Brilliant NLP. What the Most Successful People Know, Say and Do.* Harlow: Pearson Education.

Murray, C. and Lopez, A. (1996). *The Global Burden of Disease.* Cambridge, MA: Harvard University Press.

Mynors-Wallis, L., Moore, M., Maguire, J. and Hollingbery, T. (2004). *Shared Care in Mental Health.* New York: Oxford University Press.

Neighbour, R. (2005). *The Inner Consultation. How to Develop an Effective and Intuitive Consulting Style*, 2nd edn. Oxford: Radcliffe Publishing.

O'Connell, B. (2005). *Solution-Focused Therapy*, 2nd edn. London: Sage Publications.

O'Hanlon, B. and Weiner-Davis, M. (2003). *In Search of Solutions. A New Direction in Psychotherapy.* New York: WW Norton.

Pendleton, D., Schofield, T., Tate, P. and Havelock, P. (2003). *The New Consultation. Developing Doctor–Patient Communication.* Oxford: Oxford University Press.

Rai, G., Rosenthal, J., Morris, J. and Iliffe, S. (2006). *Shared Care of Older People.* Edinburgh: Elsevier.

Rollnick, S., Miller, W.R. and Butler, C.C. (2008). *Motivational Interviewing in Health Care. Helping Patients Change Behaviour.* New York: The Guilford Press.

Royal College of Psychiatrists (2009). *The management of patients with physical and psychological problems in primary care. A practical guide. College Report CR152.* London: Royal College of Psychiatrists.

Scanlan, M. (2010). *Read yourself well. A qualitative exploration of prescribed bibliotherapy.* Essex University: Doctoral Thesis.

Seligman, M.E.P. (1998). *Learned Optimism. How to Change Your Mind and Your Life.* New York: Free Press.

Tate, P. (2010). *The Doctor's Communication Handbook*, 6th edn. Oxford: Radcliffe Publishing.

Williams, C. (2003). *Overcoming Anxiety. A Five Areas Approach.* London: Hodder Arnold.

Willson, R. and Branch, R. (2006). *Cognitive Behavioural Therapy for Dummies.* Chichester: John Wiley and Sons.

Williams, M., Teasdale, J., Segal, Z. and Kaba-Zinn, J. (2007). *The Mindful Way Through Depression.* London: The Guilford Press.

Yapko, M. (1997). *Breaking the Patterns of Depression.* New York: Broadway Books.

Yapko, M. (2009). *Depression is Contagious.* New York: Free Press.